V3

For Martin

by the same illustrator

THE OWL AND THE PUSSY-CAT

by Edward Lear

DID YOU EVER?

Gwen Fulton

JONATHAN CAPE
THIRTY BEDFORD SQUARE LONDON

Did you ever ever ever
see a codfish who was clever?

Or a dolphin dance a horn-pipe on his tail?

Or a flounder play at skittles?
Or a pig that left his victuals?

Or a porpoise
sit and whistle on a rail?

Or a double-breasted badger?

Or a really starving cadger?

Or a hermit who lives
happily on roots,
one who daily feeds
and fattens?

Or a pelican in pattens?
Or an ostrich in knee-breeches
and top-boots?

Or a rosy-visaged baker?

A white-hatted undertaker?

Or a cap that wouldn't fit a dozen boys?

Or a pea-green dromedary?

Or a quiet cock canary?

Or a cobbler who all his time employs?

Or a jackdaw pass a spangle?
Or an oyster turn a mangle?

Or a cabman knocking
gently at a door?

If you've had your attention
drawn to half the things I mention,
you've seen what never
has been seen before.

Horn-pipe

Sailor's lively dance

Hermit

One who lives alone
and eats simply

Spangle

Jewellery;
or glittering object

Flounder

Small flat-fish

Pattens

Raised wooden soles
used to protect shoes
from mud

Mangle

Roller press
used in laundry

Skittles

Bowling game using
bottle-shaped pins

Visage

Face

Cadger

Seller of butter and eggs;
or beggar

Victuals

(pronounced 'vittals')
Food

Dromedary

Camel with one hump

Cabman

Driver of a hired cab
or carriage

First published 1981 Jonathan Cape Ltd, 30 Bedford Square, London WC1 Illustrations © 1981 by Gwen Fulton
British Library Cataloguing in Publication Data Fulton, Gwen Did you ever? I. Title 398.8 PZ8.3 ISBN 0-224-01740-3
Printed in Great Britain by W. S. Cowell Ltd.